W9-BVP-289

I SPY
FUNNY TEETH

For Chalupa,
with great thanks to Dan
—J.M.

For Elizabeth Helt
— W.W.

Text copyright © 2003 by Jean Marzollo.
"Toy Chest," "Make Believe," "Odds & Ends," and "Cubbies" from *I Spy* © 1992 by Walter Wick; "Peanuts and Popcorn" and "The Laughing Clown" from *I Spy Fun House* © 1993 by Walter Wick; "A Whale of a Tale" and "The Hidden Clue" from *I Spy Mystery* © 1993 by Walter Wick; "Yikes" from *I Spy Fantasy* © 1994 by Walter Wick; "Mapping" from *I Spy School Days* © 1995 by Walter Wick.

Library of Congress Cataloging-in-Publication Data
Marzollo, Jean.
 I spy funny teeth : riddles / by Jean Marzollo ; photographs by Walter Wick.
   p. cm.
Summary: Simple text challenges the reader to find objects hidden in the photographs.
ISBN 0-439-52472-5
 1. Picture puzzles — Juvenile literature. [1. Picture puzzles.] I. Wick, Walter, ill.
II. Title.
GV1507.P47 M355 2003
793.73 — dc21   2002015495

ISBN-13: 978-0-439-52472-8
ISBN-10: 0-439-52472-5
50 49   19
Printed in the U.S.A. 40 • This edition first printing, August 2008

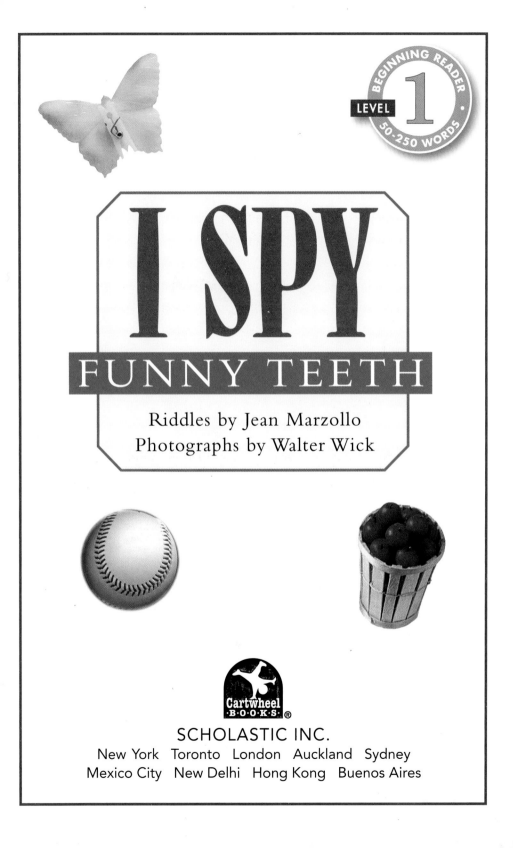

BEGINNING READER

LEVEL 1

50-250 WORDS

I SPY

FUNNY TEETH

Riddles by Jean Marzollo
Photographs by Walter Wick

Cartwheel
·B·O·O·K·S·®

SCHOLASTIC INC.
New York Toronto London Auckland Sydney
Mexico City New Delhi Hong Kong Buenos Aires

I spy

a car,

a kazoo,

a horn,

a number game,

and a box of popcorn.

I spy

a tank,

 two baseballs,

a clock,

 a frog in a truck,

and a blue wooden block.

I spy

a guitar,

 a fish,

a bow tie,

 a face,

an axe,

and a butterfly.

I spy

sunglasses,

a mask that's dark blue,

a clock,

a fan,

and a pink purse, too.

I spy

a green star,

 an apron that's white,

a truck,

 a jack,

and a red flashlight.

I spy

two gas pumps,

 a maze,

a bear,

four pink flowers,

and a clown's yellow hair.

I spy

a spoon,

 a basket of fruit,

two birds,

an S,

and a cowboy boot.

I spy

a giraffe,

 a marble,

 a king,

two googly eyes,

 and a blue-stone ring.

I spy

a domino,

 a big yellow Y,

funny white teeth,

 and a red bow tie.

I spy

five hats,

three M's,

an E,

a musical note,

and a zebra Z.

I spy two matching words.

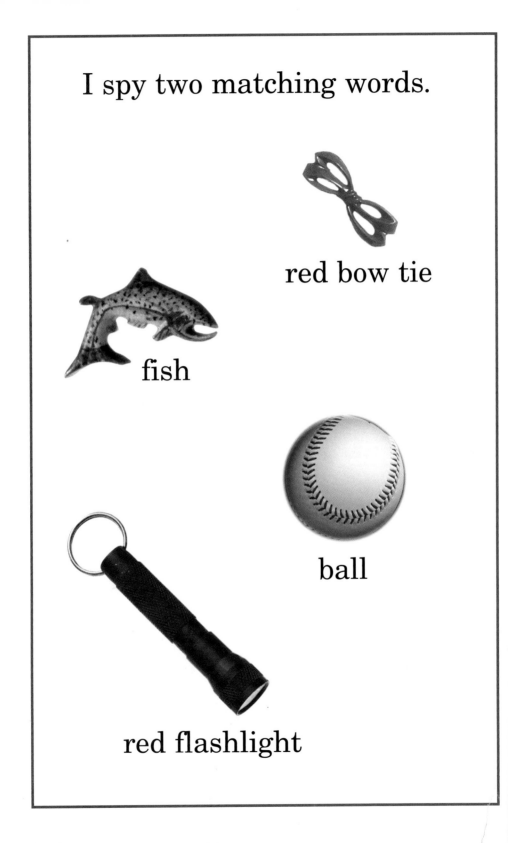

red bow tie

fish

ball

red flashlight

I spy two matching words.

guitar

blue block

bus

blue mask

I spy two words that start with the letter B.

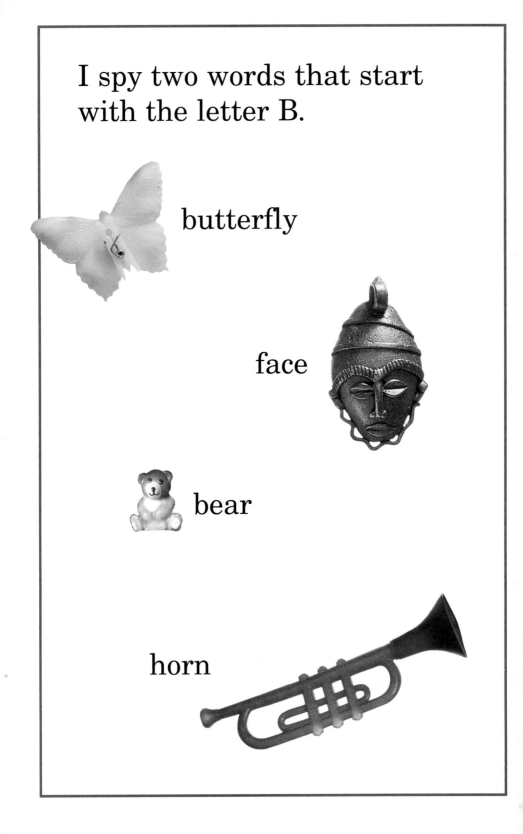

butterfly

face

bear

horn

I spy three words that start with the letter P.

two gas pumps

 boot

pink purse

 truck

I spy two words that end with the letter S.

teeth

two googly eyes

car

two birds

I spy two words that end with the letters CK.

jack

game

zebra

truck

I spy two words that rhyme.

yellow Y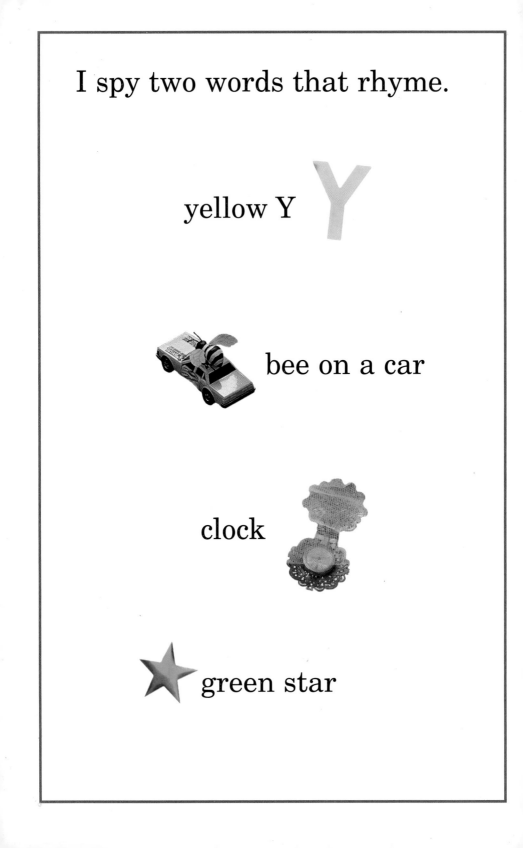

bee on a car

clock

green star

I spy two words that rhyme.

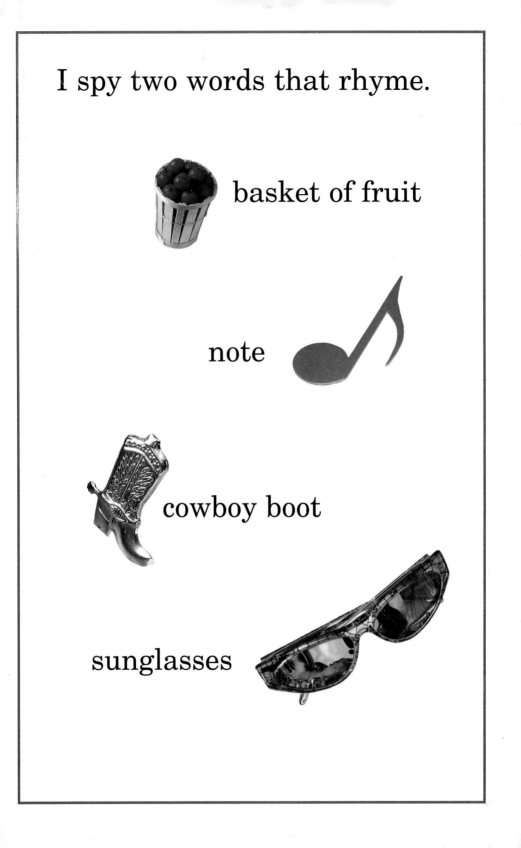

basket of fruit

note

cowboy boot

sunglasses